But where shall wisdom be found?
and where is the place of understanding?

The depth saith, It is not in
and the sea saith, It is not wit
The Book of Job 28: 12, 14

Sand tiger shark.

Contents

Credits

Text	Stephen Spotte
Graphics	Joseph O'Neill

Photographs provided by staff members of Mystic Marinelife Aquarium

Patricia M. Bubucis	Research Technician
George A. Cassidy	Volunteer Coordinator
Alan Desbonnet	Special Program Coordinator Education Department
Charles R. Hatch	Volunteer
Mike Johnson	Aquarist
Laura E. Kezer	Director of Community Relations
Gayle Sirpenski	Aquarist
Stephen Spotte	Director
Jim Stone	Assistant Curator of Education

MYSTIC MARINELIFE AQUARIUM

Published by
MYSTIC MARINELIFE AQUARIUM
Division of Sea Research Foundation, Inc.,
a non-profit organization dedicated to education and research.
Mystic, CT 06355 USA
©1986 Sea Research Foundation, Inc.
ISBN-0-915897-05-9

Overleaf: Smallmouth grunts on a Caribbean coral reef.

Introduction

The Aquarium's dual purpose is to interpret the natural history of aquatic organisms through education, and to further the understanding of how aquatic organisms live in water through research.

Our purpose determines everything we do and how we do it. The epigraph on page 1, written centuries ago by an unknown hand, has lost none of its meaning. Where indeed shall wisdom be found? And where is the place of understanding? As you walk through the Aquarium, be aware of the information being transmitted. Note that the creatures before you are depicted in settings that simulate their native habitats. Take time to read the overhead graphics, which supplement the sensory information your eyes and ears assimilate from close contact with the animals and plants. Seek wisdom from your experience. The Aquarium is an instrument of knowledge, one place of understanding.

Some people believe it is morally wrong to keep animals in captivity. They claim that confinement somehow takes away the dignity of living wild creatures, shortens their life-spans, interrupts their breeding cycles, and causes them to suffer psychological anguish. None of these accusations is true. The life-spans of most animals are actually lengthened by captivity. Wild animals seldom die of "old age." Animals that become infirm are preyed on by stronger ones, or they succumb to parasitism and disease. These factors can be controlled in healthy captive environments. Many captive animals — seals and sea lions here at the Aquarium, for example — breed regularly and produce normal, active pups. Evidence of psychological anguish, as demonstrated by abnormal behavior, is not seen in properly designed facilities.

The matter of dignity has been saved for last. Mystic Marinelife Aquarium and institutions like it are engaged in a desperate race to save wildlife. The race is being run in two lanes. In the first lane are the educators committed to teaching people about the importance of wildlife and the need to protect wild habitats. The biggest habitats of all are the oceans. In the second lane are the researchers. A great deal of what we know about animals has been learned from captive specimens. The information gained can often be applied to management of wild populations, ultimately assuring their safety. We see our work as critical to formulating effective conservation programs worldwide. If we fail, species will become extinct. What "dignity" is there in extinction?

View of the waterfowl pond looking south.

Humpback whales feeding off Cape Cod, Massachusetts.

History

Mystic Marinelife Aquarium opened in October 1973 and at first was operated as a privately owned, profit-making corporation (Mystic Aquarium, Inc.). The principal shareholder was Mr. Kelvin Smith, a Cleveland industrialist and philanthropist. Operating expenses were met by revenue from admissions, annual memberships, and gift shop sales. Mr. Smith later donated funds to construct two major outdoor exhibits. Seal Island, which cost $3 million, was opened in July 1977. A Steller's sea lion exhibit at the front entrance can be viewed free of charge during public hours. It was built at a cost of $365,000 and opened in June 1979.

In September 1977 Mr. Smith established Sea Research Foundation, Inc., a nonprofit organization dedicated to education and research. Its first assets included the building and grounds of Aquarium of Niagara Falls (New York), which he owned. Institute for Aquarium Studies in Hartford, Connecticut, was established as a branch of the Foundation in November 1977. The Institute, which conducts research on management of small aquariums, employs two persons and was relocated at Eastern Connecticut State University in July 1983. Mystic Aquarium, Inc. was dissolved effective 30 April 1979. Its entire $2.6 million debt was paid by Mr. Smith, who previously had bought out the rest of the shareholders. The buildings, grounds, and other assets became part of the Foundation on 1 May 1979.

In 1983 the front entrance of the main building was expanded to streamline movements of incoming visitors. The project took 16 weeks and included a new two-story gift shop and bookstore. Sales space was increased from the previous 840 square feet to 2500 square feet. Costs of construction and furnishings were paid out of earned income. Profits from retail sales are returned to the Aquarium's operating budget to help support education and research programs.

Living Exhibits

The main floor of the Aquarium houses 43 exhibits of living aquatic animals and plants, ranging in volume from 30 to 30,000 gallons. The majority are marine; only a few freshwater organisms are displayed. Two themes are emphasized: *Adaptation* and *Aquatic Communities*. Each exhibit in the *Adaptation* section illustrates a single mechanism that an animal or plant has evolved to enhance survival, which in turn allows it to reproduce and propagate the species. The yellowhead jawfish, for example, burrows into the sand for protection and defends its burrow against intruders, including other jawfish. The anemonefish counts on a sea anemone's stinging tentacles to protect its eggs from predators. Other organisms utilize camouflage, schooling, or some different mechanism to gain a competitive edge.

Exhibits in the *Aquatic Communities* section depict specific habitats with indigenous animals and plants. Emphasis is on species collectively, instead of individually as in *Adaptation*. Undersea terrains of the communities displayed are reproduced in fiberglass-reinforced plastic as a weight-saving measure (see Exhibit Preparation). Thus an exhibit of New England's coastline includes striped bass and tautogs (representative fishes), kelp and rockweed (typical plants), and simulated boulders of gneiss, schist, and granite (principal rock forms of the region). Exhibits of tropical ocean habitats include colorful reef fishes and simulated reef-building corals. The living exhibits are subject to change.

Artificial Seawater

Every known element is dissolved in the oceans, but comparatively few serve known physiological functions and are required by marine animals and plants. The Aquarium is located too far up the Mystic River estuary to pump seawater, and artificial seawater must be used instead. Staff scientists devised a formula known as *GP2 Medium*. The elements provided in the formula are listed in the table. The letters "GP" stand for "General Purpose."

Composition of artificial seawater

Chloride	Bromide	Iron
Sodium	Carbon	Iodide
Magnesium	Nitrogen	Manganese
Sulfate	Strontium	Molybdenum
Calcium	Borate	Zinc
Potassium	Phosphate	Vanadium

Curators and aquarists in the Exhibits Department mix GP2 Medium in mixing vats of 15,000 gallon capacity using dry salts in carefully weighed amounts and ordinary tap water. After 24 hours of aeration the solution is suitable for maintaining the most delicate fishes, *invertebrates* (animals without backbones, like crabs and sea anemones), and seaweeds.

Filtration

The living exhibits are filtered individually by *subgravel filters*. These consist of perforated plates covering the bottoms of the aquarium tanks. Each plate is supported underneath by spacers to keep it above the bottom. Gravel spread on the plate is the filtering material, removing particulate matter and metabolic wastes generated by the animals and plants.

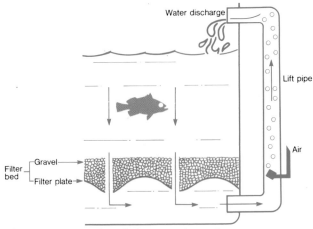

The water in each exhibit circulates from top to bottom. Circulation is provided by *airlift pumps*. Airlifts operate on a simple principle: water entering the pipe from underneath the filter plate is mixed with air injected from the main compressors. The air-water mixture, being lighter than water alone, rises to the top of the pipe where it spills out at the surface. Thus aeration, filtration, and circulation are accomplished simultaneously, provided that the flow of air continues uninterrupted.

Supplementary Information

The living exhibits are supplemented by graphics, scientific labels, audiovisual programs, and free-standing displays. The purpose of this additional information is to reinforce and interpret themes illustrated by the plants and animals. Overhead graphics focus on a principle of nature, often by comparing it with an analogous human situation. Scientific labels identify the organisms. Sound programs explain facts like the possible origin of the word "shark," and typical slide presentations elucidate how the Aquarium operates or how a marine food chain functions. A major free-standing display is entitled "What is a Fish?" and depicts by graphics and tactile experience (i.e., visitors can touch portions of the display) the enormous diversity of fish: reproduction, size, and types of scales are examples of themes dealt with. Supplementary information, like the living exhibits, is subject to change.

Exhibit Preparation

A new exhibit is not simply "set up" as one might a home aquarium. Adding a new exhibit or changing an old one involves *exhibit preparation*, and the process is more complicated than the result suggests. First a theme is chosen (*camouflage*, for example), and a suitable location is selected. Camouflage illustrates an adaptive principle, and the location therefore must be the *Adaptation* section. Curators in the Exhibits Department (the department responsible for all living and nonliving exhibits) meet to decide which specimens best illustrate the principle. They agree that a fish known locally as the sea raven is ideal. Sea ravens are ordered from a professional collector or an Exhibits Department team is dispatched to collect them (see Acquisition of Specimens).

When sea ravens lie motionless on the bottom they look like moss-covered rocks. Rocks with lush growths of Irish moss (actually not a moss but a seaweed) are collected. Gravel to cover the bottom of the exhibit tank is shoveled from a local beach, poured through sieves, and washed. Sections of the exhibit that require large boulders are measured. Local rocks are picked for texture, shape, and size, and latex molds are made from them. The rocks are cast in fiberglass-reinforced plastic. During casting, pigments are added to duplicate the natural coloration of the original surfaces. Finished "rocks" are cured with dry heat for 24 hours to drive off volatile residues that might be toxic to marinelife.

The subject of camouflage in marine organisms is researched in the Aquarium library. If needed, additional material is obtained from libraries of the University of Rhode Island and the Marine Biological Laboratory at Woods Hole, Massachusetts. Text is written from the research material, and sketches of a proposed graphic are made. Curators in the Education Department check for grammar, sentence structure, accuracy, and educational value. Final text is set in type, and the graphic is finished by a staff artist or graphics consultant. If sea ravens have not been displayed previously, a new scientific label must be painted by a staff artist and a color transparency made of the finished artwork.

The gravel is shoveled carefully into the exhibit tank, and "rocks" are arranged in a pleasing manner. Artificial seawater is added, and the temperature is adjusted to local ocean temperature. Sea ravens prefer cold water, and a refrigeration unit must be plumbed into the exhibit by the Engineering and Maintenance Department and tested for several days. Overhead lights are adjusted for angle and intensity, and a proper flow of air is established. Finally the sea ravens and the Irish moss they so closely resemble are placed in the exhibit. Everything is finished, but the process has taken several weeks and involved dozens of specialists.

Acquisition of Specimens

Animals and plants for the living exhibits are collected by the Exhibits Department, purchased from dealers and professional collectors, and donated by local fishermen. The Aquarium holds collecting permits for the marine waters of Connecticut, Rhode Island, and New York. Collection is done by seining, setting fish traps, SCUBA diving, and trawling.

Tiny anemone shrimp living in the stinging tentacles of a sea anemone.

Venomous lionfish.

Orange tube corals expanded at night.

Cluster of sea stars.

Giant Pacific octopus.

Common squid.

Rare blue lobster.

Venomous fireworm.

7500-gallon Caribbean Coral Reef exhibit. Corals are artificial and cast by Aquarium artists.

Foureye butterflyfish.

Schoolmasters.

Blackbar soldierfish.

French angelfish.

Trout exhibit.

Wharf's End exhibit.

Offshore Waters exhibit.

Foods for fishes and invertebrates.

Preparing a new exhibit with artificial corals.

Feeding the exhibit fishes.   Capturing a shark.

Collecting specimens in cold New England waters.

Seal Island

Seal Island is located to the east of the main building and connected by a footbridge. In terms of architecture and innovative technological features Seal Island is unique; there is no comparable exhibit anywhere in the world. Seals, fur seals, and sea lions (collectively called *pinnipeds*) are displayed in 3 exhibits each with its own pool, tidepools, beaches, and steep cliffs of artificial rock (see Unique Features). The exhibits are entitled *New England Coast, Pribilof Islands*, and *California Coast*.

Harbor seals and gray seals, the only species of pinnipeds indigenous to New England, are displayed in *New England Coast*. Only northern fur seals are exhibited in *Pribilof Islands*. The Pribilofs are a cluster of small islands 225 miles north of the Aleutian Islands of Alaska in the Bering Sea. California sea lions and northern elephant seals, which range along the coasts of California and northern Mexico, are the pinnipeds showcased in *California Coast*.

Water and Filtration

Unlike dolphins and whales, which need salt to keep their skins healthy, pinnipeds do just as well in freshwater. Water for Seal Island originates from a freshwater well. Incoming water pumped at 80 gallons per minute enters a *header* (main distribution line) that disperses it to the pools. From there it is collected in another header and directed to a bank of 4 filters each 9 feet in diameter. Sand and anthracite coal are the filtrant materials, and water is circulated by a 40-horsepower cast-iron pump with stainless steel impeller. An identical pump is on standby if the first suffers mechanical failure. Filtered water in excess of the volume required empties into a waterfowl pond located between Seal Island and the main building. In summer the pools are refrigerated by two 40-ton refrigeration units that start automatically when the water temperature exceeds 65°F (18°C).

A hospital pool measuring 10 feet square by 4 feet deep is located in the service building off exhibit. The pool is used as temporary quarters for newly-captured or sick animals. The water is filtered separately from the main system by two steel pressure vessels 5.6 feet in diameter. Filtrant materials are sand and anthracite.

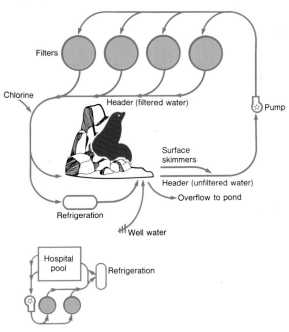

Unique Features

The beaches of Seal Island are composed of natural cobbles embedded in a concrete matrix, then stained. Other pinniped exhibits ordinarily are constructed of smooth concrete, which is then painted. The result is unnatural and featureless. The backs of the exhibits are bounded by cliffs of artifical rock. The cliffs average 22 feet in height and are constructed of Glas-Con, a combination of concrete and fiberglass. This material is lighter and stronger than conventional concrete. To make the artificial cliffs, latex rubber molds were taken from a natural cliff, cut into sections of 55 square feet, and transported to a warehouse in Mystic. Here, the molds were filled with Glas-Con reinforced with steel rods. When the concrete hardened

the molds were stripped away, and the panels were numbered for erection in the proper sequence to maintain natural crevice lines. Each panel weighs approximately 670 pounds and is 1 inch thick.

To erect the Glas-Con cliffs a crane held each panel in a vertical position while the reinforcing rods were welded to others embedded in the concrete walls of the exhibits. Spaces between panels were wired with steel mesh and filled with gunnite (a type of concrete), which was tooled while still soft so that the seams matched the surface relief of adjacent panels. Afterward the cliffs were stained a uniform color.

The tidepools of Seal Island are another feature not duplicated elsewhere. Their purpose is to provide shallow areas where newborn pups can practice swimming in relative safety. In other pinniped exhibits the edge of the beach area often ends abruptly at a pool filled with deep water. The young of all pinnipeds can swim weakly at birth, but many are unable to climb out if they fall into deep water. The outer perimeters of Seal Island's tidepools are supported by concrete pilings, which are connected by spans of fiberglass-reinforced epoxy grate. The grate is hidden by layer of loose cobbles, which still permits water to circulate through.

Breeding Program

A primary reason for building Seal Island was to maintain breeding colonies for pinnipeds. By keeping the animals in large, open exhibits subject to nature's seasonal cycles it was hoped that all species would breed and rear their young, thus providing important biological data that could otherwise be obtained only with great difficulty from wild populations. Overall the program has been remarkably successful. Events of note include the first live captive birth of a northern fur seal, ninth captive birth of a northern elephant seal (the pup was stillborn), and birth of the first gray seal twins to survive to weaning either in the wild or captivity. Harbor seal and California sea lion pups are born every spring and summer. After weaning they are transferred to other institutions, thus reducing the number of animals taken from the wild.

Acquisition

Many of the adult California sea lions and all of the northern elephant seals were originally beach-stranded and later acquired from West Coast rehabilitation centers. The younger California sea lions, harbor seals, and gray seals were captive-born in Seal Island. The older northern fur seals were captured during Aquarium expeditions to Alaska in 1977 and 1984; the younger ones were acquired from rehabilitation centers in northern California and Washington State. A few specimens were donated by other institutions or obtained in trades. California sea lions trained to perform in the Marine Theater sometimes are "retired" to Seal Island when they become too large.

Veterinary Care

The seals and sea lions are weighed regularly and examined by a consulting veterinarian. A sick animal is placed in the hospital pool off exhibit until it recovers. Blood samples are taken and a program of medical treatment is established. All animals are vaccinated periodically against pasteurellosis, a bacterial disease.

Gray seal.

Harbor seal and pup.

New England Coast exhibit.

Feeding the harbor seals.

Aquarist with friendly harbor seal.

Gray seals in the snow.

Pribilof Islands exhibit with northern fur seals.

Educational graphics at Seal Island.

Capturing a northern fur seal in Alaska.

Vaccinating a seal pup.

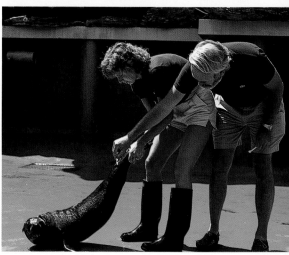

Female northern fur seals with pup.

Northern fur seal pups.

Construction of artificial cliffs at Seal Island.

Feeding a northern elephant seal.

Weighing animals at Seal Island.

Feeding a Steller's sea lion.

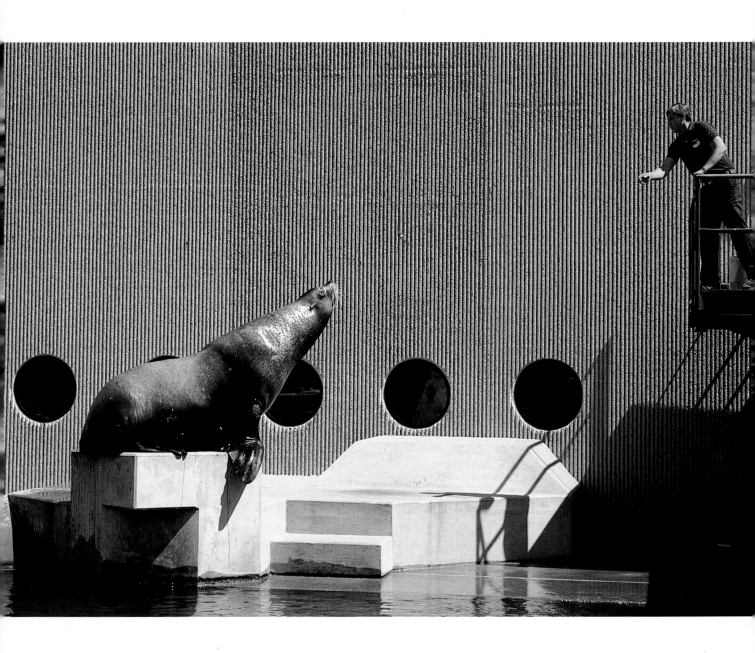

...aining a Steller's sea lion to dive on command.

Steller's Sea Lions

The Steller's sea lion exhibit is located at the entrance to the Aquarium. Steller's sea lions can be seen at just one other institution in North America, because they are large and aggressive and require special display techniques. Mature males sometimes attain weights of more than 2000 pounds; females are smaller, averaging 700 pounds at full growth. The species was named in honor of George Wilhelm Steller, an 18th century naturalist. The exhibit is separated from viewers by a large, dry moat. Trainers and handlers feed the animals from an elevated platform. Training demonstrations are conducted regularly throughout the day.

The dry portion of the exhibit measures 889 square feet. The pool is 35.5 feet by 20 feet and averages 9.5 feet in depth. The volume of the pool is 63,000 gallons. Water is supplied continuously from a freshwater well and recirculated through a single steel pressure filter 8 feet in diameter. A female pup born in June 1983 was only the fifth live birth of a Steller's sea lion in captivity.

Freshwater Wetlands

View of the waterfowl pond looking west.

Feeding the waterfowl.

Barnacle geese.

Two waterfowl ponds are located between the main building and Seal Island. Several species of ducks, geese, and swans are displayed. The birds are *pinioned*. To pinion a bird the tips of the bones on one wing are clipped off. That wing does not develop flight feathers, and the bird is unable to fly. Pinioning is practiced in all aquariums, zoos, and nature reserves to keep valuable breeding birds from escaping.

The ducks on exhibit are species that once were abundant in southern New England until excessive hunting and habitat distruction limited their numbers. The Aquarium's duck-breeding program is designed to permit some of the young to fly away each spring after they fledge. The practice should help to repopulate the region with species that are rarely seen in the wild like pintails, wood ducks, redheads, and canvasbacks.

A freshwater marsh, accessible to visitors by a boardwalk, is located adjacent to Seal Island. A low concrete wall separates it from the larger waterfowl pond. The source of water to the marsh is a manmade stream designed by Kanje Domoto, a Japanese landscape architect. Water is pumped from the larger waterfowl pond to the head of the stream on the low hill behind Seal Island, from which it flows by gravity through a rocky bed into the marsh. Excess water spills back into the waterfowl pond.

The marsh contains a thriving stand of cat-tails, swamp irises, and other wetland plants established by the Exhibits Department. It supports a breeding population of eastern painted turtles that in summer can be seen sunning on the banks. Other free-ranging wildlife includes redwing blackbirds, barn swallows, cowbirds, dragonflies, bullfrogs, and mallard ducks. The marsh is used extensively as a nesting site by pinioned waterfowl and serves as an abundant food source for ducklings that rely heavily on aquatic insect larvae and daphnia (water fleas) during their first weeks out of the nest.

Mute swan and koi carp.

Marine Theater

Whales and dolphins (collectively called *cetaceans*) are exhibited in three adjoining pools. The largest is referred to as the *main pool*. It is elliptical and measures 40 feet in width, 70 feet in length, and is 20 feet deep. The main pool is flanked by two cylindrical holding pools. Both are 27 feet in diameter and 9 feet deep. The holding pool nearest the Aquarium entrance is the *south pool;* the *north pool* is in view of the Laboratory. Total volume of the tri-pool complex, including filters and pipes, is 410,000 gallons.

The walls of the pools are poured concrete, steel-troweled to a smooth finish. Corners are rounded to facilitate scouring by water returning from the filters. The walls are 12 inches thick. The surface coating is epoxy paint, refinished every other January by staff members who volunteer their time from all departments. Scraping and repainting the main pool takes a week, with teams working around the clock.

The windows (six in each holding pool, five in the main pool) offer underwater viewing. Each window is polished acrylic, 5 feet square by 2.25 inches thick. Visitors in the 1400-seat Marine Theater on the second level can view the whales and dolphins from above the surface. The pools are illuminated from overhead by eight 1000-watt mercury vapor lamps and 12 750-watt quartz lamps.

Water Treatment

Whale and dolphins are air-breathing mammals. Lacking gills, they are no more dependent on the chemical composition of water than a human swimmer. Complex artificial seawaters like GP2 Medium are not required to maintain cetaceans in good condition. They simply need sodium and chloride to keep their skins healthy. The Aquarium's cetaceans are kept in a solution of municipal tap water and table salt (sodium chloride). The latter is pumped into the pools as concentrated *brine* from large dissolving units located behind the scenes.

Water clarity is maintained by continuous addition of *alum* (aliminum sulfate), which coagulates tiny particles of matter in the water column to form larger *aggregates*. Eventually an aggregate becomes large enough to be trapped in the filters. Aggregates are removed from the water system when the filters are backwashed into the sanitary sewer.

Water in the tri-pool complex is disinfected by continuous addition of sodium hypochlorite, the active ingredient of which is chlorine. Chlorine kills potentially harmful microorganisms and perhaps hinders transmission of infectious diseases through the water. The eye irritation experienced by human swimmers in chlorinated pools is caused by nitrogen trichloride, a reaction product of chlorination. This compound does not form if the water chemistry is rigorously controlled, as it is by Aquarium technicians.

Filtration

Water in the tri-pool complex is filtered by eight high-rate sand filters. These are large, steel pressure vessels measuring eight feet in diameter. The filters are powered by four 8-inch, 40-horsepower, admiralty bronze centrifugal pumps. The tri-pool complex is processed by four sets of filters, each consisting of two filter

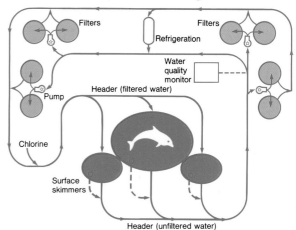

units and one pump. Turnover of water through the entire system is once every 90 minutes. Valves are arranged so that any pool can be emptied for repair or to examine an animal without affecting circulation and filtration in the other two pools. A pool is isolated by inserting a watertight bulkhead made of laminated fiberglass-reinforced plastic and balsa into a common channel with the adjacent pool. Afterward the water in the isolated pool is restricted to passing through a single set of filters, and none mixes with the rest of the system.

Marine Mammal Demonstrations

Demonstrations of animal behavior are presented hourly in the 1400-seat Marine Theater by staff members of the Training Department, who are experienced in handling whales, dolphins, and California sea lions. Each demonstration lasts about 30 minutes. Unlike facilities that stress "showmanship," the Aquarium's policy is to emphasize natural forms of behavior. This presents a more realistic picture of how animals in the wild behave. Wild dolphins do not wear hats or play basketball; rather they *breach* (jump out of the water and land on their sides), *porpoise* (break the surface rhythmically to breathe), *sound* (dive beneath the surface), and leap. The Aquarium's whales and dolphins execute these natural exercises on command. California sea lions are trained to perform behaviors that illustrate their remarkable sense of balance and motor coordination.

Animal Training

Marine mammals are trained by a technique called *operant conditioning.* The principle is simple: when an animal is rewarded for doing something, chances are good it will repeat that behavior. The reward must come at the instant the desired behavior is executed. When training whales and dolphins this is not always possible because an animal may be in the middle of the pool, or even underwater. A *conditioning stimulus* in the form of a police whistle is used instead. Blowing the whistle lets an animal know it has performed correctly and will be rewarded with a fish. Sea lions are trained on land, and the trainer is close enough to make a conditioning stimulus unnecessary. Training any animal is painstaking. A trainer *shapes* the behavior he wants by dispensing a reward each time progress is made toward a predetermined goal.

Capture and Transport

Most cetaceans are obtained by Aquarium capture teams, but an occasional whale or dolphin is purchased or obtained in trade with another aquarium. Belukha whales are captured in the Canadian arctic at the mouth of the Churchill River on the western shore of Hudson's Bay. The term *beluga whale* is incorrect; a beluga is a fish — specifically a Russian sturgeon — and not a mammal. To catch a belukha the capture team flies to the town of Churchill. No roads lead there across hundreds of miles of flooded tundra. Capture must occur in late July or early August when ice in the river breaks up. The ice starts to form again in early September. Any capture attempt must include participation of the native people, who are mostly Cree Indians and Inuits. Whales are driven into shallow water by wood canoes powered by outboard engines. The capture team selects a young adult belukha of about 800 pounds and wrestles it onto a stretcher. The stretcher is positioned in a larger canoe for the trip back to shore, where the animal is placed in a portable swimming pool. After a day or so of observation the whale is put onto a stretcher inserted in a watertight box and flown to New York by chartered aircraft. From there it is transported the remaining 100 miles to Mystic by refrigerated truck.

Dolphins are captured in Florida waters and transported by the same technique. The usual procedure is to surround a group of animals with a 300-foot net in water less than 20 feet deep. The net is played out from the stern of a fast boat. When the dolphins are encircled, swimmers release the unwanted specimens. The remaining dolphins are placed on wet foam on the deck and rushed to a fenced lagoon near shore. After a short observation period they are flown to Connecticut.

Veterinary Care

Diseases take a major toll of wild marine mammals. Captive specimens benefit from veterinary care and the latest antibiotics. As a result, they often live longer, healthier lives than their counterparts in the oceans. The cetaceans are given quarterly physical examinations by the consulting veterinarian and vaccinated twice annually for protection against erysipelas, a bacterial disease. The animals are weighed, and blood samples are drawn at each examination. The blood profile of each animal is compared against normal values. As in humans, blood testing is a useful tool in preventive medicine. Abnormal values are sometimes indicative of infectious disease, hormone imbalance, major organ malfunction, and other maladies that can be life-threatening.

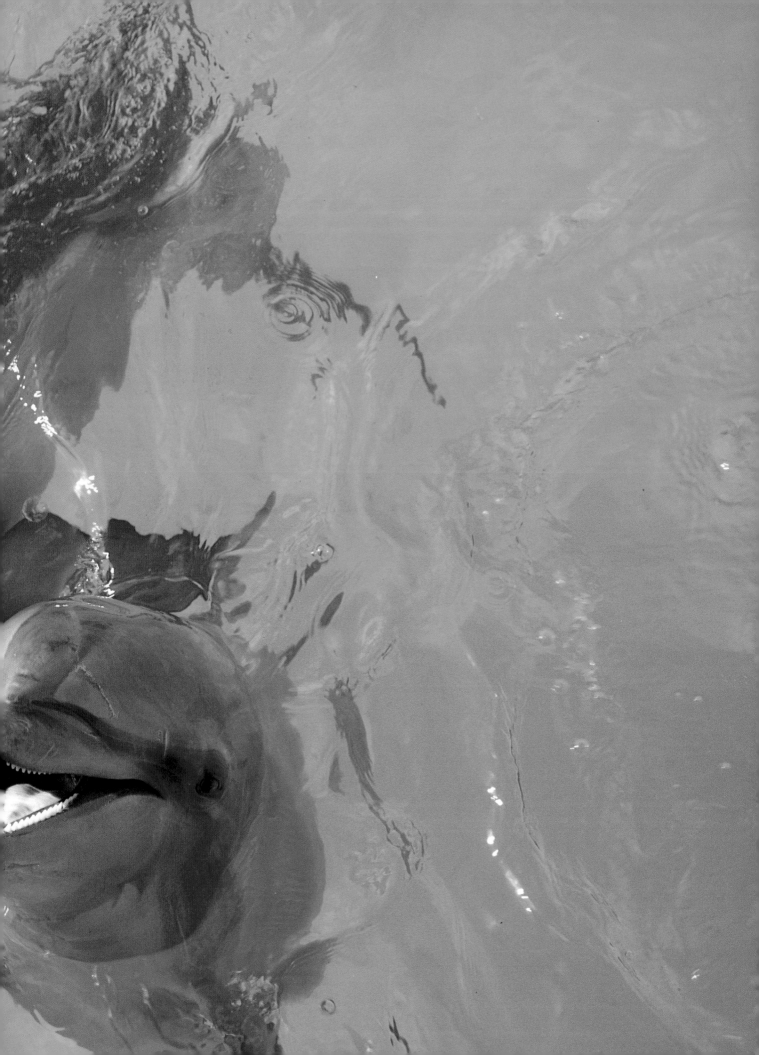

Performing belukha whale.

On stage with a trained California sea lion.

Cutting fish for the performing animals.

Whale and dolphin pool filters.

On stage with the trained Atlantic bottlenosed dolphins.

Capturing a belukha whale in the Canadian arctic.

Carrying a newly captured belukha whale.

Preparing an Atlantic bottlenosed dolphin for transport.

Education

The Aquarium is recognized throughout the country for its innovative education programs. The Education Department offers programs in natural history designed to supplement conventional classroom instruction in the life sciences. These are available to students of all ages, pre-school through the university level. It is the Aquarium's position that an interest in science is fostered initially in children through direct contact with living plants and animals. Through this type of first-hand contact, which is supplementary to the standard science curriculum, students are often stimulated and motivated to pursue careers in science.

Each year 60,000 students representing 1200 schools visit the Aquarium, and 30% participate in organized classroom instruction, often combined with marine-oriented field experience. Outreach programs bring natural history to an additional 15,000 students annually in Connecticut, Rhode Island, and Massachusetts. Other services include evening classes in adult education, accredited undergraduate and graduate courses at the university level, classes and field trips for members and their children, programs for students with special needs (e.g., hearing-impaired, gifted-and-talented), and student internships. The Aquarium also serves as a resource center for all of southern New England.

Classroom education.

Research

The Aquarium is more than an exhibit; it also is a living laboratory. Every animal and plant displayed and every aspect of the captive environment is a potential subject for research. The research effort focuses on applied natural history, emphasizing development of methods to extend the longevity of aquatic organisms in captivity. Results are published in international journals where they are available to scientists around the world. Some of the published data are used by aquaculturists for intensive rearing of fishes in Third World countries where protein is in short supply. Other findings are applied to breeding programs for endangered species and thus contribute toward conserving the living resources of the earth.

The research team includes full-time staff members and adjunct researchers from nearby industries and universities. Expertise and facilities consequently are expanded far beyond the physical and financial limits of the Aquarium itself. Adjunct scientists are experts in such critical fields as marine microbiology, animal nutrition, marine bioacoustics, fish pathology, analytical chemistry, computer science, chemical engineering, and electron microscopy.

Captive Environments

Captive aquatic environments typically are polluted with the metabolic products of plants and animals, mainly ammonia and dissolved organic carbon. In fish these substances limit growth, lower reproductive capacity, and reduce immunity to infectious diseases. No similar effects in marine mammals have been found, but research nevertheless extends to water systems used to maintain cetaceans and pinnipeds. Studying captive environments requires the use of sophisticated analytical chemistry, because some metabolic pollutants are toxic at concentrations of less than one part per million parts seawater. After these compounds are identified and quantified, chemical engineering methods are applied in pilot studies to determine how to remove them rapidly and economically.

Marine Mammal Biology

The Aquarium's captive colonies of marine mammals are extensive: six species of pinnipeds and two species of cetaceans are exhibited, totalling approximately 60 animals. The Research Department and its adjunct scientists have contributed toward furthering understanding of how marine mammals are adapted for life in the oceans. The captive environment offers unique opportunities for research that would be impossible to duplicate using wild specimens. All research is noninjurious, as demonstrated in the following examples.

The daily food intake of eight adult female northern fur seals at Seal Island was monitored for a year, and the seals were weighed periodically. It was discovered that the animals regulated their food intake (and therefore body weight) seasonally, eating more between late autumn and late spring than at other times of the year. The information obtained matched findings of a researcher in British Columbia, Canada, who at the time maintained the only other captive colony of northern fur seals in the world. The results may be important to wildlife biologists in management of wild populations. Previously it had been assumed that northern fur seals consume relatively fixed percentages of their body weights daily. Northern fur seals compete with commercial fisheries in the North Pacific Ocean and Bering Sea. The Aquarium's research suggested that any impact on fisheries, based on government reports of how much fur seals eat, may be in error by thousands of tons annually, simply because seasonal feeding variation was unaccounted for.

Twin gray seals were born at Seal Island in December 1980. They were rejected by the mother at birth. Abandoned seal pups ordinarily starve, but staff members succeeeded in hand-rearing these pups to weaning, marking the first time twins of any species of pinnipeds had been hand-reared, and only the second known occasion in which twins survived, either in the wild or in captivity. (Twin harbor seals were reared by their mother at Stanley Park Zoo in Vancouver, British Columbia in 1978.) During the rearing process considerable data were collected, enabling researchers to estimate the food requirements of unweaned gray seals.

Rescue and Rehabilitation

For centuries people have wondered why cetaceans occasionally beach themselves, ultimately to die. The answer still is not known. Once a whale or dolphin becomes beach-stranded the odds of it surviving are poor. Nevertheless the Aquarium's policy is to pick up stranded cetaceans, provide medical care, and attempt to rehabilitiate them for ultimate return to the ocean.

The *Marine Animal Rescue Team* consists of Training Department personnel, the consulting veterinarian, and volunteers from other departments with a keen interest in working with sick animals and a high tolerance for cold, lack of sleep, and other discomforts. Most strandings in New England occur in winter when working conditions are dismal.

The Aquarium is a founding member of the *Northeast Regional Stranding Network*, which includes the New England Aquarium in Boston, the Smithsonian Institution in Washington, and several smaller organizations. Our region covers the coastlines of Connecticut and Rhode Island. Concerned Aquarium members have donated vehicles, an inflatable boat, and other equipment. When a telephone call is received about an animal on a beach, the leader of the rescue team is notified immediately, day or night. Equipment is always packed and ready to go, because timing is crucial: a stranded cetacean's chances of survival ebb with every minute ashore. The team rushes to the stranding location with blue light flashing and loads the unfortunate animal onto a stretcher. During the return trip anti-shock drugs are administered by the consulting veterinarian, and a cursory medical examination is performed. Meanwhile members of the Engineering and Maintenance Department have inserted a watertight bulkhead between the north and main pools, isolated the north pool on a single set of filters, and lowered the water level. The possibility of an infectious disease being transmitted to the resident cetaceans is thus minimized.

The rescue team arrives at the loading dock, and the stretcher is quickly coupled to a hoist and lifted to the second floor. The consulting veterinarian takes blood samples and swabs for microbiological culture to ascertain if an active infection is present. Some blood is processed immediately in our laboratory; the rest is sent to professional testing labs. Swabs are delivered to the Marine Science Laboratory of the University of Connecticut in Noank, where marine microbiologists isolate and identify the organisms and measure their sensitivities to different antibiotics. If necessary, medical opinions are obtained from researchers and clinical practitioners at Pfizer Central Research in Groton and Lawrence and Memorial Hospitals in New London.

Another hoist lifts the cetacean in its stretcher over the railing and lowers it gently to the water below. Divers release the animal and "walk" it as long as necessary to ease cramped muscles. Within 24 hours a medical program is devised and implemented according to data obtained from blood and microbiological work. The next step is to induce the animal to eat, either by force-feeding it or offering live and dead fish.

The mortality of beach-stranded cetaceans exceeds 95% in the first 90 days, but occasionally a specimen beats the odds. A young female harbor porpoise named Puffin lived at the Aquarium for nearly 2 years, after having been recovered from a local beach in critical condition. Puffin provided much valuable information about her species and proved to be as interesting and trainable as her poolmates, the bottlenosed dolphins. To save an occasional Puffin makes up for the cold, the lack of sleep, the worry, and finally the anguish when a rescued cetacean dies.

Two Atlantic white-sided dolphins were found beach-stranded on Cape Cod in the winter of 1983. The male (subsequently named Harvey) stranded in early December; the female (called B.J.) came ashore 10 days later. Both animals were brought to the Aquarium where they recovered from the initial trauma within a few days. B.J. died in April 1984 of a pulmonary abscess. Harvey recovered completely. On 11 April 1984 he was released near a group of white-sided dolphins feeding off Montauk Point, Long Island. Staff members cheered and waved farewell as Harvey joined the other dolphins and disappeared with them in the direction of the open sea.

Microbiology research.

Phytoplankton research.

Counting plankton cells in the Research Laboratory.

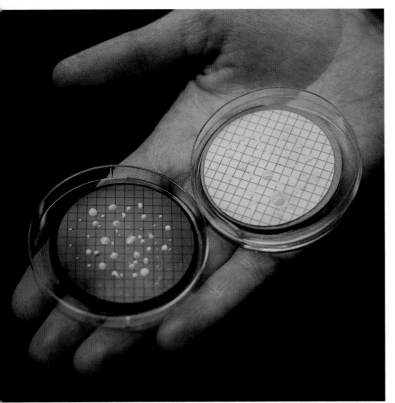

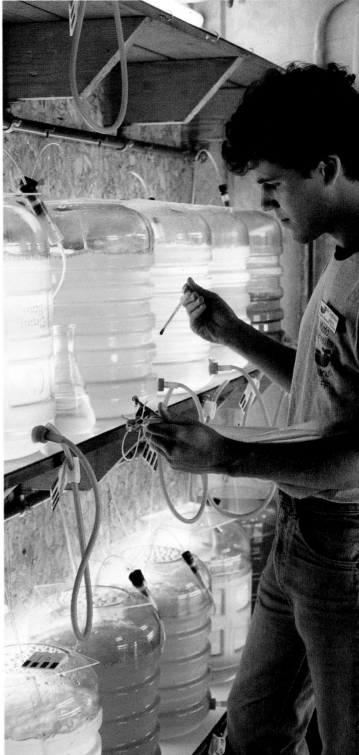

Egg case emerging from a chain dogfish.

Chain dogfish depositing her egg case.

Development of the embryo at 17 days.

Development at 97 days.

Development at 147 days.

Development at 188 days.

Development at 229 days.

Newly hatched chain dogfish, aged 248 days.

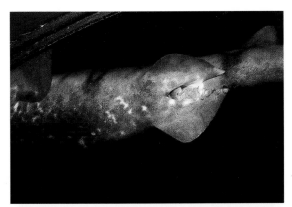

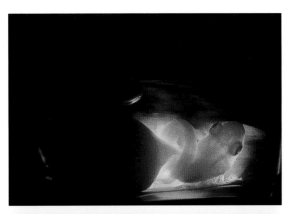

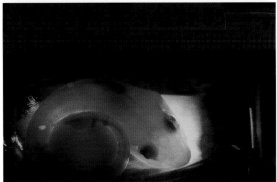

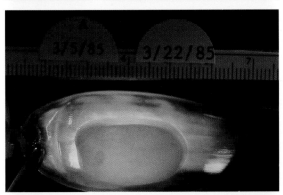

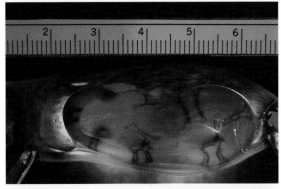

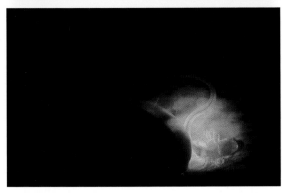

Rescue of rare white-beaked dolphins from pack ice in Newfoundland, Canada.

Rehabilitating Harvey, a beach-stranded dolphin. Harvey was later released off the tip of Long Island, New York.

Longfinned pilot whales stranded and dying on a New England beach.

Aerial view of Mystic Marinelife Aquarium looking northwest. The main building is to the left, Seal Island to the right.

Production and Design by
Fort Church Publishers, Inc.
and Donald G. Paulhus

Printed in Japan.